IT'S ALL ABSOLUTELY FINE

IT'S ALL ABSOLUTELY FINE

LIFE IS **COMPLICATED** SO I'VE DRAWN IT INSTEAD

RUBY ELLIOT

TRAPEZE

For Nina and Harry and Miranda, just . . . yes?

For Mum and Dad, who I've known pretty much all my life and have, despite everything, always kept the house filled with so much laughter and nuttiness and love and pens. You're alright I guess.

And also for Sam, who we miss very much.

THIS IS A MAGICAL EDITH.
WE DON'T KNOW WHY,
BUT SHE IS.

CONTENTS

INTRODUCTION BIT

Hello, my name is Ruby and that's about as far as I can get before I start worrying about what to say next. To give you a bit of context, here are some other names I go by:

RUBY: EMOTIONAL CESSPIT, THE 9TH WONDER OF THE WORLD

BIG BAG OF TEARS

PRINCESS SARCASMO

NO REALLY,
THAT'S GREAT

A POTATO

So yes, I'm a pretty versatile disaster as you can see. What I've essentially done for this book is draw about the stuff that goes on in my head, and stuff that goes on outside of my head, and how those things mush together in a bit of a strange and confusing way. They are drawings about me, but I hope that some of them may be about you too. And if not, that's fine, the book will work nicely as a sort of deluxe rectangular coaster. Everyone's a winner.

IT'S A
BEAUTIFUL DAY
FOR DON'T

I **am sitting on the floor next to the bed waiting for nothing to happen.** The blinds are closed because I cannot stand the light and the way it makes people want to be outside doing talking and laughing and interesting things with their lives. The last activity I did was dragging myself on all fours, slug-like, to the kitchen and sprinkling sugar straight out of the bag onto a piece of old bread, then standing by the counter cramming it into my face like I was a VHS on fast forward. If I don't feel real then why would I bother feeding myself as if I were? I've been wearing the same pyjamas for years, centuries, well, a week really but the level of stale is probably sufficient for them to be sealed in a glass case and put on one of those little plinths in a museum. I imagine tour guides pointing out the various unidentifiable stains (a mixture of snot, tears and canned soup) to a group of confused tourists taking polite photos – 'And here we have a garment dating back to a 4 year long depressive episode'. There could be a little plaque. And a gift shop selling postcards, except they're just bits of old pizza box torn up into postcard size with UGH scribbled on them in crayon.

The first time I experienced major depression was aged 16. I'd already been very unwell for a couple of years with an eating disorder that had left me miserable and often hospitalised. But this was different, this was as if an actual steamroller driven by a crazy grinning idiot had trundled through the door and flattened my entire life into a sad pancake of nothingness. It wasn't that I stopped caring about life, but I stopped being able to care. My brain, having been suspended in a state of hyper-vigilance for such a long time, just packed in and said 'No more, your job now is to lie on the sofa incredibly still and just work on evaporating, you useless trowel'. And so I did.

For months and months I spent all day and all night curled up in a variety of mildly uncomfortable positions on my parents' sofa, creating a small arse-shaped dent in one of the seat cushions and wearing the others down until they looked as deflated and sad as I felt. And you know what? It was shit. It was very shit for a long time. No one wants to be lying there at 3:30am reciting the entirety of a Ped Egg commercial ad verbatim as it plays for the fifth time in a row because you haven't had the energy to change the channel. No one wants to be permanently on the edge of bawling because their reality is one of life being utterly futile and pointless. No one wants to feel so desperate that they end up on a psychiatric ward being asked to rate their mood on a scale of 1-10 as they watch their laces being yanked out their shoes and taken somewhere out of reach. But these were all things that happened to me because I was depressed.

My dog was the first person to get me out of the house during the sofa months. I mean, there are only about two things in the world that can make me go outside when I am at my most dysfunctional – the first of which came to light when I was living alone and had run out of loo roll (doesn't matter how low I felt, at some point I was going to have to wee) and the second was my woofular unit needing a walk. Aged 16 I was acutely insecure and paranoid about other people seeing me, but clipping the dog's lead on and having her bounce along beside me sniffing the pavement and pissing on trees distracted me from the crushing weight of my own negative thoughts. She was like a mobile security blanket except better and funnier with barking, and a brilliant reminder that it is possible to just 'be'. It's for this reason that animals are excellent to have around, particularly when you're feeling shit, because they are so untroubled by existence and unwaveringly confident in their ability to enjoy stuff (even if that stuff is rolling in fox poo). When I was unwell, all the care and kindness I wasn't able to offer myself I could defer onto the dog, and it was in loving the very simple, very stupid, incredibly happy ball of fur and ears I could find just a little bit of point in the pointless.

That's what you need sometimes, whether it's a dog or a cat or a jazzy lizard or something else entirely that provides you with some emotional re-spite when it's all too messy – a tiny yet significant port in an almighty storm.

TODAY I FEEL LIKE A VERY
TERRIBLE PEBBLE

HERE IS ME, ON THE BEACH OF LIFE. I'M NOT EVEN ONE OF
THE NICE PEBBLES SOMEONE WOULD PICK UP AND SAY
"OOH, THAT'S A NICE PEBBLE" AND TAKE ME HOME.
JUST HURL ME RIGHT INTO THE CHOPPY SEA

EMOTIONAL SMOOTHIE
RECIPE

INGREDIENTS:

COUPLE GLOBS OF UNSPECIFIED
YET WEIGHTY SADNESS

AHHHHHH

A GOOD WOK'S WORTH
OF FEAR & CONFUSION
(WHY IS IT A WOK? NOBODY
KNOWS, THAT'S PART
OF THE TERRIBLE MYSTERY)

BAG OF ANXIOUS
EXCITEMENT THAT'S ALL
SPLIT DOWN THE SIDE
AND SPILLING EVERYWHERE

CAN O' EXHAUSTION
INDUCED TEARS

LONELINESS MEASURED OUT
IN THAT ONE WEIRD SPOON
EVERYONE HAS THAT DOESN'T
MATCH THE REST OF THE
CUTLERY

ONE VERY TINY TENTATIVE
PINCH OF HAPPINESS AND
HOPE (OR HOWEVER MUCH
YOU CAN TOLERATE)

<u>METHOD</u>:

CRAM INGREDIENTS INTO BLENDER

BLEND UNTIL GRITTY AND WEIRD. YOU'RE
AIMING FOR A TEXTURE THAT'LL STICK IN
YOUR THROAT AND MAKE
YOU FEEL LIKE YOU'RE
VAGUELY
SUFFOCATING

POUR INTO A GLASS AND ADD
ONE OF THOSE STUPID TINY
UMBRELLAS, FOR STYLE

ENJOY!

I DON'T WANT TO HEAR IT

FOR THE LAST TIME THESE AREN'T **TEARS**,
THEY ARE **GLAMOUR BEADS** THAT JUST
HAPPEN TO BE FALLING FROM MY EYES IN MY FACE

WAITING FOR THE VOID

OH LOOK HERE IT
COMES NOW

TURN THAT FROWN

SIDEWAYS

GO OUTSIDE

TERRIFY THE PEOPLE

THE SOUNDTRACK TO MY LIFE

AAAARGHH

NOTHING. I. DO. IS. EVER. ENOUGH

BANG   BANG   BANG

LADY LOOK, I'M VERY BUSY HERE CRUSHING MY OWN SELF ESTEEM CAN YOU PUSH OFF?

POP!

AH! BUT I AM THE INSIGHT FAIRY

..HAVE YOU CONSIDERED THAT THIS "ENOUGH" MAY BE SYMBOLIC OF A DEEPER UNDERLYING SENSE OF INADEQUACY AND FAILURE TO MEET THE UNATTAINABLE HIGH STANDARDS YOU'VE SET YOURSELF IN LIFE..

..AND THAT PERHAPS NO MATTER HOW MUCH YOU WERE OBJECTIVELY DOING, YOU WOULD STILL FEEL DISSATISFIED, BECAUSE TO FEEL CONTENT WOULD SOMEHOW EQUATE WITH COMPLACENCY AND LAZINESS..

I DON'T THINK YOU EVEN KNOW WHAT "ENOUGH" IS.
I THINK YOUR PERCEPTION OF ACHIEVEMENT IS SO
SKEWED BY YOUR LOW OPINION OF YOURSELF THAT
YOU FIND IT EASIER TO STAY SUSPENDED IN A STATE
OF MILD TO MODERATE DISCONTENT BECAUSE AT LEAST
THEN YOU CAN PRETEND YOU HAVE   ANY
IDEA OF WHAT IS GOING ON

TICKLE
TICKLE

I'M GOING TO LIE DOWN
PLEASE WAKE ME UP IN
A COUPLE OF DON'T

YOU KNOW WHEN PEOPLE SAY "THEY'VE THROWN ME IN AT THE DEEP END"?

YEH

AND IT'S MEANT TO BE SCARY? BUT IF YOU WERE THROWN IN AT THE SHALLOW END

YOU'D PRETTY MUCH JUST SMACK YOUR HEAD AND DIE!

ARE YOU OKAY?

YES, PROBABLY NO

WE ARE GOOD AND WE ARE OKAY YES SIR

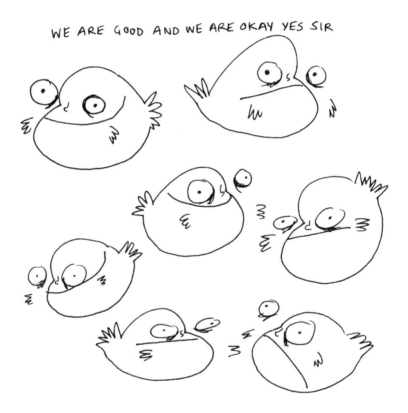

AVOIDANCE TECHNIQUE #582:

"EVERYTHING IS A YES OR NO QUESTION"

OF COURSE THE BASIS FOR THIS AVOIDANCE IS NOT LAZINESS, BUT SIMPLY ME BEING SO PROFOUNDLY UNHAPPY AND DISAPPOINTED WITH THE STATE OF MY LIFE AND MYSELF THAT IT'S EASIER TO RESORT TO FACETIOUSNESS THAN WADE 6FT DEEP INTO MY OWN MENTAL TURMOIL EVERY TIME I'M ASKED A QUESTION.

IS THIS A BAD DAY

OR ONE IN A SERIES OF MANY

IS THIS A DIP

(NOT A DELICIOUS ONE : SOME KIND OF STALE SADNESS HUMMUS)

OR AM I TEETERING ON THE EDGE OF SOMETHING

MUCH MORE UNTOWARD

I WISH I COULD TRUST MY OWN JUDGEMENT

I WISH IT WAS EASIER TO KNOW

SO WHY CAN'T I JUST DO WHAT EVERYONE ELSE IS DOING?

IF THEY'RE ALL STARTING HERE, HAVING MENTAL ILLNESS IS LIKE BEING BURIED DEEP UNDERGROUND. I HAVE TO TUNNEL UPWARDS IN THE DARK JUST TO REACH EVERYONE'S NORMAL BASELINE OF FUNCTIONALITY

IT'S SO FRUSTRATING, HAVING TO LIE THERE KNACKERED AND COUGHING UP SOIL WHILST EVERYONE ELSE DANCES OFF INTO THE WORLD

I'VE BEEN DIGGING AND DIGGING, BUT I CAN STILL FEEL LIKE A FAILURE. I CAN STILL FEEL LEFT BEHIND.

IF YOU'VE GOT FUCK ALL DONE TODAY

BUT YOU'VE BEEN THINKING
ABOUT THE ALL

CONSIDERING
IT

LETTING IT RUN
THROUGH YOUR MIND
A BIT

THEN THAT IS OKAY

CONSIDER YOURSELF BUFFERING

LOAD TOMORROW

A NICE DRAWING OF WELL-MEANING ME DRAGGING RELUCTANT, DESPONDENT ASSHOLE ME EVERYWHERE

MY HAPPY CORNERS

FOAMY COFFEE WITH
THE CHOCOLATE NONSENSE

A PARK BENCH WHEN
IT'S COLD AND BRIGHT

DRAWING SOMETHING SILLY
WHILST I SING AND DO A
LITTLE DESK WIGGLE
DANCE TO A WHOLE
KATE BUSH ALBUM

HEATHCLIFF!
IT'S ME
YOUR
CATHY
I'VE COME
HOME

I KNOW THESE ARE PLACES
I CAN GO WHEN I'M NOT
OKAY. THESE ARE MY SAFE
SPACES; MY HAPPY CORNERS

HOW TO BE

① FROWNY

② HELLO

③ WHAT?

④ IT IS SIMPLE

HEY, YOU ARE BRILLIANT.
KNOW THIS.

BEP!

MAKE THINGS

EXCUSE ME
WHILE I RUIN EVERYTHING

ACCIDENTALLY

ON PURPOSE

SLOW
SMUSH

why are you doing that?

JUMPY
JUMPY

SMUSH
SMUSH

I DON'T KNOW
I DON'T KNOW
IT'S JUST
HAPPENING

SMUSHY
SMUSHY

JUMP
JUMP

THERE, NOW
EVERYTHING
IS RUINED

I DO NOT

PARTICULARLY UNDERSTAND

WHY IT IS
NECESSARY

FOR ME, MYSELF

TO BE SUCH AN
ALMIGHTY SHIT

MNEH

GOT ME A NICE PRESENT
FOR ME!

HMM.. I COULD ACKNOWLEDGE THE
THINGS I'VE ACHIEVED AND THE
STUFF THAT'S GONE WELL.. YES..

OR!

I CAN USE THIS UNDERMINEOSCOPE
TO MAGNIFY ALL MY SHORTCOMINGS
AND S THINGS I COMPLETELY
FUCKED UP ON

A DELIGHT

SORRY..

FOR WHAT?

EXISTING

I DON'T
KNOW..
THE THING

THEN WHY ARE
YOU APOLOGISING?

SORRY
SORRY

ARE YOU APOLOGISING
FOR APOLOGISING?

YES.. SORRY..
WAIT.. NO

UGHHHH

I'M JUST GONNA GO.. IF YOU
NEED ME I'LL BE IN A BIN OVER THERE
FOR THE REST OF MY LIFE

SOMETIMES I SLOW
DOWN

AND I BEGIN
TO THINK

ABOUT WHAT'S
GOING ON. ABOUT MYSELF
AND WHAT I'M DOING

BECAUSE I'VE BEEN
AVOIDING IT OF LATE

AND BEFORE I'VE HAD
A CHANCE TO TELL
MYSELF I'M FINE

I NOTICE A HOLE
APPEARING

AND ALL THIS EVERYTHING BEGINS
TO SPILL OUT

GOD THERE IS SO MUCH

I FEEL SO SMALL IN THE FACE OF IT

AND INSTEAD OF GATHERING IT
ALL UP

HURRIEDLY STUFFING IT BACK IN
SO NOBODY, INCLUDING MYSELF,
HAS TO SEE IT

... FUUUUUCK

STUFF   IN
STUFF

I LET IT HAPPEN

I FEEL

AND I AM VULNERABLE NOW

SOMETHING'S BEEN PUNCTURED

EVERYTHING'S SURFACING

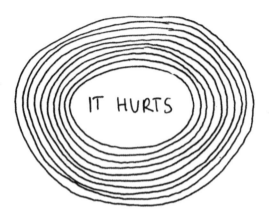

AND I DON'T

I DON'T WANT

TO GET RID OF IT

I DON'T WANT TO
RUN

I WANT TO RIDE
THIS OUT

I'M GOING TO RIDE THIS OUT BUT IT'S SCARY

AND I'M SO SCARED

TODAY'S LOOK

NOT STRONG ENOUGH TO DEAL WITH
MY OWN INEPTITUDE

I **am well practised in the art of fucking myself over. If self-sabotage** was an exam I'd pass with flying colours and then stare at my result blankly for 7 minutes before scrunching it up and throwing it at the bin because UGH, I should have passed with colours more flyingly and it doesn't change the fact I'm a terrible person and in fact everything about me is wrong please excuse me while I leave town to go and live in a cave.

You know the thing – those moments where something goes mildly wrong in the day so you think 'bollocks to this' and cancel plans you were looking forward to in order to sit at home feeling miserable; receiving a compliment that you don't feel you deserve so you either deny it profusely or grit your teeth and smile while it is filed away under 'things I can use to beat myself up with later'. Then there's neglecting to shower or eat or go to bed before 5am because you can't quite bring yourself to look after you properly even though you *know* it's what is good for you. The tendency to do things that might sabotage us physically or emotionally exists to one degree or another within a lot of people I reckon.

So what gives then? One of the reasons I've struggled so much with this has been due to an inability to tolerate uncertainty and the 'grey areas' that life is full of. My brain used to say that if things weren't going to go *absolutely perfectly*, and if I wasn't **absolutely perfect** then they were destined to be a **total disaster** and **so was I**. Any perceived threats to this state of 'perfection' would cause me to shut down and instantaneously commit to things being awful. There was no middle ground – no concept that things could be kinda alright and a little bit rubbish at the same time. And crucially, my brain said if they were definitely going to be awful anyway then fuck it, *I might as well launch myself there headfirst first before anything out of my* *control has the chance to do it*. That's self-sabotage: undermining yourself because at least then the outcome is predictable – bad, but in my control.

Combine this with terrible self-esteem and mental illness and we've arrived at one of the tabooiest of taboos – self-harm. A lot of people will never come close to experiencing anything like it, but a lot of people, including myself, will. It's one of the aspects of mental health people find 'unpalatable' and uncomfortable to consider, and so discussion around it is often silenced, or else reduced to misrepresentative media depictions of teenage 'cries for help' with all the attendant implications that it is an attention seeking or selfish behaviour; nothing more than a phase (I need to employ a proxy to do my eye rolling for me whenever I hear that stuff being said because my face is too exhausted at this point). Yes, it is baffling trying to get to grips with how anyone could possibly override the need to self-preserve in order to voluntarily cause themselves pain, but this should not be more important than the suffering of those who feel they have to spend years concealing that pain while they become experts in thinking up creative answers for 'What are those marks on your arm?'. This is why I talk openly about what I've been through. Because the silence is exhausting and isolating in a way it needn't be.

Self-harm is not an uncommon experience, nor is it a shameful defect or personal failure, it happened to me because I wasn't able to manage intense emotional distress. It had the very specific function of turning an intangible and relentless mental pain into an acute and quantifiable physical one, which temporarily (because it was always temporary) alleviated some of the distress I was in. And frankly, given the levels of shitstorm going on in my mind at the time, I held onto any relief I could, even if it was via self-sabotage. There were logical reasons to my illogical behaviour, based on feelings about myself and my situation that may not have been the reality, but were incredibly real and scary to be experiencing.

I'M TRAPPED BUT IT'S SAFER IN HERE THAN WHAT'S GOING ON OUT THERE

There is no neat little paragraph for how I broke the cycle of punishing myself for my brain punishing me – I wish there was. It's actually been pretty messy and boring. It took a long time to arrive at a place where I even wanted to take an active role in my existence, let alone working through enough stuff in my own mind and in therapy to feel I might deserve something other than self-destruction. But the point is that you can arrive at that place. I'm not going to use the phrase 'finding alternative healthy coping mechanisms', not because it's untrue, but because it's one of those things that's been said at me by professionals so many times it makes me want to scream just a tiny bit a lot.

Preventing self-sabotage is a very personal act, and I had to develop my own ways of doing this. Some came about organically over time and others were hops and leaps of faith I had to trust might work and be more sustainable than the trauma I was putting my brain and body through (even if in the short term they felt rubbish and difficult to tolerate). So here are some bits of that; a few of my routes out:

· It's unrealistic to expect myself to go from 'I loathe myself beyond words' to 'I love and value me 'cos I'm worth it *hair swish*' overnight. I can take jazzy little lizard steps towards compassion at my own pace

· Self-soothing takes work, but it doesn't have to be outrageously positive or anything. Sit-down-'n'-cry-in-the-dark showers are surprisingly effective

· As is painting my nails obnoxious colours

- And listening to very loud music through headphones while I do my best and most stunning foetus impression under the duvet

- And hugging the dog, because she is a dog

- Whichever form of potential self-sabotage I'm up against, putting distance between me and the act is important. In a very practical sense, not having the means to wreck things available to me or removing myself from the immediate situation if it's getting dodgy gives me a bit more breathing space

- Because urges do pass. They do. They pass

- If I've written the word 'fuck' all over a piece of paper then scribbled it in black, I feel a bit better

- I don't have to view my experiences in any way I don't feel is right for me. I don't choose to put any quasi-positive spins on self-harm like it 'made me a stronger person' or think of my scarring as beautiful 'signs of survival'. I'll be indifferent about it if I want. I'll be sad about it if I want. I'll place focus on it when I want to and not when I don't

- Similarly – I don't apologise. I don't owe anyone an explanation or justification and if people have a negative opinion or issue with scar tissue then they can sod off really

- Reminder that if I am going to punch the wall I need to put a pillow between it and my fist before doing so (swollen bruise hands and scrapey knuckles are not a great look)

- Horrible times or feelings don't have to be counteracted with more horrible, and I can't always contain it on my own. **It's okay.** And I am allowed to text/ring/email/fax/send a messenger pigeon to someone and ask for help before it all goes completely to piss. That is a good thing to do

- There is very little in life that is All or Nothing and I'll learn to tolerate grey areas, it's possible but it just takes bloody ages (I've made it through this whole piece without using the word bloody for obvious reasons but I've caved here because it's a good word and I like it)

- It can be the end of the world, sure, but it won't be this way forever.

WHY WOULD I WANT TO TAKE BABY STEPS? BABIES ARE SHIT AT
WALKING. THINK ABOUT IT

TO MOVE FORWARD I'LL BE TAKING JAZZY LITTLE LIZARD STEPS

TOGETHERNESS

ALTERNATIVE
SELF-CARE

SURROUND YOURSELF WITH LIZARDS; YOU ARE
THE QUEEN NOW

SMASH A CROISSANT INTO A WALL

DIP YOUR ELBOW IN CANDLE WAX
AND RUIN ALL THE CANDLES AND NOW
THEY LOOK HOW YOU FEEL AND IT IS
A FUN TIME

IT IS IMPORTANT TO
NOTICE WHAT YOU HAVE
DONE WELL

IT IS ALSO IMPORTANT TO
NOT LET THINGS YOU
MESSED UP UNDERMINE
THE THINGS YOU DID DO WELL

THE TWO CAN CO-EXIST

HOLD ON TO YOUR
ACHIEVEMENTS

ARTICULATE DOG

GOOD DAY

GOOD DAY AFTER A
STRING OF BAD DAYS

MAYBE I _AM_ CAPABLE

HAHAHA

5 GOOD THINGS ABOUT ME

I.   I LIKE DOGS

b)   SOMETIMES MY EYEBROWS LOOK NICE

iii   THIS ONE TIME I WALKED HOME WITHOUT A SINGLE BUS GOING PAST WHICH MEANS I WON

IV   DOGS LIKE ME

Fig5   I HAVE ALLTWO OF MY ELBOWS

6.   I AM EXCELLENT AT COUNTING AND STUFF

PEP TALK

HEY

YER DOING ALRIGHT,
DID YOU KNOW
THAT?

PEP

PEP PEP

THANK
YOU
THAT IS A NICE

I'M DOING MY STUFF
EVERYONE ELSE'S STUFF
CAN FUCK OFF

MAGICKEN

SEE THE MAGIC
SPARKLE IN HER
BEAUTY EYE

SO,
HOW ARE YOU
FEELING
TODAY?

USEFUL VISUAL INDICATORS OF HOW
I'M FEELING WHEN WORDS WON'T HAPPEN

THE RAIN

MOULDY OLD
BREAD

SHITTY CHILD'S DRAWING
OF A HUMAN

BAD SOCK DRAPED
OVER THE BACK OF
A RADIATOR

BALLOON UNKNOWINGLY
WAFTING TO WARDS SOMETHING
POINTY

I THINK WHAT WE KNOW IS THAT YOU HAVE THE TENDENCY TO BE QUITE IMPULSIVE..

I WAS WONDERING WHETHER YOU HAD ANY THOUGHTS ON THAT?

MMM?!

UNNECESSARY SHOPPIN

MORE UNNECESSARY SHOPPIN

YOU ARE HAVING
AN ILLNESS

OK, SO HOW LONG
WILL THIS GO ON
FOR?

MEHDUNNO.. COULD
BE ANY TIME BETWEEN
NOW AND WHENEVER
IT ENDS

BUT THERE'S A
TREATMENT?

YESS

BUT ITS EFFECTIVENESS ISN'T
GUARANTEED AND IS ALSO LARGELY
DEPENDENT ON HOW MUCH WORK
YOU PUT IN

BUT I'M SO TIRED FROM
HAVING THE ILLNESS AND
NOW I HAVE TO WORK?!
FOR SOMETHING THAT
MAY NOT WORK?

OH! THERE
ARE ALSO
SOME
PILLS

FANTASTIC!
GIMME GIMME GIMME

BUT AGAIN, THERE IS NO REAL GUARANTEE THESE WILL WORK OR BE WORTH THE MANY POSSIBLE SIDE EFFECTS - INCLUDING WORSENING OF YOUR EXISTING SYMPTOMS...

TAKE ALL THESE NICE LEAFLETS WITH YOU!

UNHELPFUL BULLSHIT

SEE YOU IN 3 MONTHS!

UNHELPFUL BULLSHIT

Right, let's get over this fear of talking about Going To Talk To Someone; because that's what therapy is by and large. When we are worried, miserable or frustrated about relatively everyday things, we may speak to someone we know, love and trust to try and alleviate the stress. But what about when you find yourself awake at 3am every night sobbing and wishing you weren't alive? Or your body feels like it's about to crumple under the weight of your own anxiety every time you leave the house? Maybe you're having weird thoughts that don't make sense and they're so loud and constant you can't really understand what's going on outside of your head. You know, stuff that is really beginning to fuck shit up. Collectively, our mental health relies heavily on supporting one another, but sometimes that's not enough. On a basic level, I think therapy is a slightly more structured way of getting what we probably all need when we are struggling, which is to talk and to be heard. So let's do away with stereotypes of shrinks and couches (I've only ever seen one once in a lifetime of therapy, and I wasn't even allowed to lie on it, it was just there like some sort of weird ornament covered in uncomfortable looking cushions). Needing therapy in itself is not that big of a deal.

A misconception that really pisses me off is that therapy is a hippy-dippy cop out for those who are too weak to deal with their problems. Nothing could be further from the truth. Being unwell is not a choice and neither is the resultant isolation, shame, guilt and conviction that you are undeserving of help that often accompany it. So actually, scraping yourself up off the floor and asking for some assistance even when every inch of your brain is screaming at you to lie there alone in your pile of brain melt is BLOODY HARD and the act of someone who is brave. It takes enormous amounts of

THERAPEST

THERAPSSHT

THERAPISS OFF

FREUD
SAYS
RELAX

THE ONE WHO ACTUALLY GETS
IT, BUT WILL INEVITABLY GO ON
LEAVE OR GET PREGNANT
          BECAUSE OF COURSE

mental effort to arrive at a place where you can ask for help, and even more to believe your problems are valid and warrant being taken seriously by a third party. I need a lie down.

I've been having therapy on and off for most of my life. And I've been through the lot in terms of therapists – the good, the bad, the ones who opt to do most of their communication through the medium of concerned eyebrows. I often consider what I could have done with the cumulative number of hours I've spent scowling on buses as I travel to and from appointments (they must be well into their hundreds). Probably could have scaled a few mountains. Or learned to play the bassoon. Or done the two simultaneously while training an antelope to crochet.

I digress...Therapy has acted as a lot of different things for me at different times in my life. Sometimes it's been a pressure valve, other times it's been a genuine lifeline. More than once I've struggled to see what its function is beyond being a giant aggravation. But for the most part it's been my fifty minutes out of the 10,080 in a week (which, by the way, is why I get so stressed about being on time) where I get to slump in a chair, and let everything unceremoniously spill out, knowing that I won't have to sit there and look at it alone.

Sure, working through the things I was in therapy for has been an integral part of the process, but actually one of the most important things I've taken away from therapy was how to use therapy and, by extension, how to allow myself to be helped. I'll explain.

I never had a problem talking about my issues (although I know this is a struggle for a lot of people); I would talk and talk until the misery cows came home about how much I loathed myself and didn't want to be here. As a teenager I would storm into the therapist's room every week like a thundercloud on angry legs and erupt with self-effacing commentary. So opening up was not the problem, knowing what to DO once I'd done that was. I remember a specific occasion where I was in a right old state – catastrophically depressed and agitated, and so immeasurably fed up with it all that I didn't want to be here anymore. This was not an unfamiliar scenario; I'd been dipping in and out of these sorts of crises for years, and doing my best to ask for help before self-obliterating. One of the most painful things about feeling very depressed and suicidal for me was the total lack of control I felt over my situation. The only thing I felt I DID have control over was my own exit strategy, and that's a pretty terrifying place for anyone to be.

So I sat opposite my therapist in floods of tears, yanking tissue after scratchy tissue out of the box between us and wishing she would take control. I mean she was the therapist after all and therapists are meant to fix you, right? Surely they have some kind of magic therapists' repository where they can scoop up and take people's distress to so that they can skip out the room afterwards, smiling and laughing and pissing rainbows? That's how it works, right? RIGHT? OH FOR THE LOVE OF GOD PLEASE MAKE THIS GO AWAY! That was the gist of the situation.

And then something hit me slightly like maybe, 1/80th of a ton of bricks: no one and nothing is going to take this away right now. What's happening is real and it's there and it's shit and I can't really control it, and wishing someone else would take it away in the knowledge they can't really do that was only making me feel more trapped and desperate. What I have got a shot at controlling is the way I manage what's happening. And that's what I was in therapy for, not to be fixed, but to facilitate and support me finding some sort of way through my difficulties. Cos you know, I can sit there in the chair for fifty minutes, but I will always have to go away and deal with the other 10,030. Those minutes are mine. And I have the capacity, if not to be a shiny happy people, to cut myself some slack when I'm suffering. And to allow the help and support in, rather than just dismiss it because I want evaporation of the ocean, not what feels like drops. Those are my minutes, my time, and even if I'm not interested in having them right now I will hold on, because the little bit of me that drags myself out the house and makes substantial dents in the therapist's tissue supply may want that later. That bit of me may grow. That bit of me has grown.

SOMETIMES I FEEL SO BIG AND FULL OF STUFF,
LIKE THERE'S NO WAY ON EARTH I COULD
POSSIBLY BE CONTAINED

OTHER TIMES IT'S THE WORLD THAT
FEELS TOO BIG AND I FEEL TINY.
EXPAND, CONTRACT, EXPAND
  CONTRACT, EXPAND, CONTRACT, EXPAND

IT'S NOT THAT I DON'T HAVE
ANY IDEAS

I'VE GOT A TON FLYING AROUND

BUT THEY'RE EVASIVE
LITTLE BASTARDS

SWIPE

SWOOSH

AND WHEN I DO GRAB ONE

IT'S SO HARD TO HOLD ONTO

SO I'M STUCK WITH THIS NOISE
OF ALL THE BLOODY BUGGERING
BIRDEAS

I CAN'T PIN ANYTHING DOWN

MY EATING PATTERNS

MY SLEEPING PATTERNS

YOU SEE BECAUSE THEY ARE
NOT PATTERNS AT ALL THEY
ARE JUST A BIG LOAD OF STUPID

I worry about nothing. Sometimes I think if I was put in a safe cube filled with only pillows and After Eights I'd still whip myself up into a total frenzy and end up on fire or something. My brain is wired to run on tangents and 'what ifs', and has a horrible habit of taking something small and snowballing it around the insides of my skull until it's twelve times its original size. That in itself is enough to be grappling with, but because this is my default setting, it means that when there ARE actually things to worry about it goes 'ALRIGHT THEN let's turn this one tier classic sponge cake of worry into a giant eighteen tier Tower of Pisa style anxiety wedding cake with elaborate piping and sparklers topped with little fondant people screaming', except actually there is no cake there's just me curled up on the floor hyperventilating because I have to go and do something that involves talking to real people and the world is almost certainly ending.

PLEASE, I AM
ONLY SMALL

GIANT TURD MOUNTAIN
OF MENTAL ILLNESS
BULLSHIT PAST AND
PRESENT

PHEW
ALRIGHT, LETS SORT
THIS OUT

. WEEKS/MONTHS OF LABORIOUS PROCESSING.
LATER ·

HAH! TAKE THAT
YOU TURD STACK

(EXHAUSTED)

RESOLVED
ISSUES

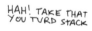

SLIGHTLY LESS GIANT
TURD MOUNTAIN OF
MENTAL ILLNESS BULLSHIT
PAST AND PRESENT

SOON!

SOON

I WILL DO IT ALL

VERY SOON

NOT RIGHT NOW COS I'M
PARALYSED BY FEAR AND
ANXIETY AND SHIT

BUT SOON!

YOU SAY "PULL YOURSELF TOGETHER"

AND THIS ONLY HELPS ME PULL MYSELF APART

IF THIS WAS SOMETHING I COULD

MYSELF OUT OF, DON'T YOU THINK I WOULD HAVE BY NOW?

BIPOLAR DISORDER

*CARTOON
FALLING FROM
A HEIGHT
WHISTLE*
NOISE

KERSPLEH

Things bipolar is

- An illness

- Massively shit a lot of the time

- One part of my life and a bit of who I am, not my entire identity

Things bipolar ain't

- **A fun, zany quirk!** – nope. I don't walk around covered in butter-flies with a cheeky twinkle in my eye, and having bipolar doesn't make me or anyone else an object of curious fascination. There is too much romanticised crap about it simply being an affliction of the tortured creative. Yes, some people with bipolar happen to make art or films or write novels while playing the harp with their toes. I guess I'm one. But I also happen to have brown hair and a wok and no one would ever say to me 'ahh yes the brown hair and having of the wok, that's GOT to be the reason you make art'. Fuck off. It's a chronic and life-affecting illness and shouldn't be treated as a novelty.

- **An adjective you can use to describe someone who's a little flighty or something that's erratic** – nopeity nope. Not clever or funny and undermines the suffering of those who are unwell. Find another word, I hear there are lots.

- **Being happy when you wake up and then maybe a bit sad and then alright again** – nah. Everyone has ups and downs, that's part of life, and it can suck and that is valid. But the moods, or mood episodes as they're called (yes, it IS like being the star of your own terrifying TV show) associated with bipolar go way beyond the bounds of what we consider to be 'normal'. Bipolar doesn't exclude me from these healthy mood swings, I get all o' those, just with the addition of very extreme lows and highs in the form of depressive and manic episodes with all their associated symptoms. It is A Lot!

MOOD STABILISERS

THESE CAN'T FIX EVERYTHING,
BUT THEY HELP ME NOT TO
TOPPLE OVER SO I CAN
CONCENTRATE ON THE PEDDLIN'

REGULAR

TIRED

LOVELY BEAUTY

OH NO OH DEAR

I'M A COMPLICATED ONE

FINDING A BALANCE

LOST:
SENSE
OF
SELF

WELL YOU KNOW HOW IT IS..

YOU HAVE YOUR GOOD DAYS

AND YOUR BAD DAYS

AND YOUR DAYS WHEN
YOU ARE SUDDENLY A LIZARD
FOR NO REASON

THAT'S JUST LIES
ISN'T IT?

KNOCK KNOCKY

WHO IS THERE?

NOT SURE, HAVING SOME SORT
OF IDENTITY CRISIS AND I
THOUGHT YOU MIGHT BE ABLE
TO TELL ME?

THAT'S NOT A
HILARIOUS JOKE

YES AND IT'S
RUINING MY LIFE

EGG

SO SMOOTH

SO
MYSTERIOUS

VERY
WISE

HAS A BETTER
SENSE OF SELF
THAN YOU

SO.. TELL ME
SOMETHING ABOUT
YOURSELF

IT'S ONLY A MATTER OF TIME BEFORE PEOPLE
REALISE I'M NOT A HUMAN I'M JUST A LOAD
OF LITTLE HUMAN-LIKE BITS BADLY HELD
TOGETHER WITH TAPE

SUPERFICIAL STUFF
LIKE BIG SHOES AND
LOTS OF EARRINGS
SO PEOPLE WON'T
KNOW HOW FRAGMENTED
AND EMPTY I FEEL

SERIES OF TWEETS
ABOUT MY DOG
OR JAM

EXCESSIVE USE OF
SELF-DEPRECATING
HUMOUR TO
COVER UP THE
FACT I DON'T HAVE
A PERSONALITY

DRAWING FOR PEOPLE SO
THE FOCUS IS SHIFTED
AWAY FROM ME ONTO PAPER

CAREFULLY CURATED
ANECDOTES I CAN USE
TO MAKE MY SMALL
AMOUNT OF LIFE EXPERIENCES
SOUND MORE INTERESTING
THAN THEY ARE

OH I DON'T BLOODY KNOW WHERE I'M MEANT TO FIT
AND WHICH PEOPLE I BELONG WITH AND WHY I HAVE
THESE SIDE NUBBINS

AT LEAST THERE'S MORE THAN ONE PIECE IN A JIGSAW.
I KNOW I'M PROBABLY NOT THE ONLY ONE WADDLING
AROUND IN A STATE OF MILD CONFUSION. IT'S
VAGUELY COMFORTING..ALMOST

NOW..CAREER PATH..BLAH BLAH..
INFORMATION IRRELEVANT TO A
15 YEAR OLD..BLAH BLAH..UNIVERSITY..
DEGREES BLAH BLAH..

SO WHAT IS IT
YOU WANT
TO DO?

...

CAREERS
OFFICERING

GET OUT

MY CV

EDUCATION: 2005-2011
A MISERABLE STRUGGLE WITH LIMITED SUCCESS

PREVIOUS EMPLOYMENT:
NOTHING THAT'LL HELP ME OBTAIN THE KIND
OF CAREER I'D LIKE

SPECIAL, SPECIAL SKILLS:
- FUCKING EVERYTHING UP
- PERSISTENT INADEQUACY
- BEING SLIGHTLY — EXTREMELY
DISHEVELLED AT ANY GIVEN TIME
- SWEARING, BOTH CREATIVELY AND
IN ABUNDANCE
- LIABLE TO BREAKDOWNS
- INABILITY TO CONTROL FACIAL
EXPRESSIONS
- THIS IS A CAT
FARTING

PFFTHHH

I'M GOING BACKPACKING ON A BIG
ADVENTURE TO DISCOVER MYSELF

I'M GOING TO MEDITATE AND
CLEAR MY MIND SO I CAN GET
BACK IN TOUCH WITH MYSELF

I'M GOING TO LEARN LOADS
OF NEW THINGS AND FILL
MY HEAD WITH INTERESTING
INFORMATION IN A REALLY
PROACTIVE WAY.

I'M GOING TO STAND INCREDIBLY STILL
AND HAVE A SMALL BREAKDOWN OVER HOW
BORING AND NOTHING I AM WITHOUT MAKING
ANY ATTEMPT TO CHANGE THINGS OR HELP
MYSELF BECAUSE HAHAHA IT'S TOO MUCH

YES, I AM SAFE HERE. YES, I AM DESPERATELY LONELY. NO YOU SHUT UP

WHEN I AM WORRIED ABOUT
SOMETHING

I JUST WORRY
ABOUT SOMETHING
BIGGER

THEN THE FIRST WORRY
WILL SEEM SMALLER

AND I'LL HAVE TWO
WORRIES AND THIS
WAS NOT HELPFUL

WHAT THE
HELL ARE YOU
DOING?

ACTIVELY ATTEMPTING
TO RELAX
AND NOT
FEEL
BAD
ABOUT
MYSELF

HOW'S
THAT
GOING?

YES,
BEAUTIFULLY AND
GREAT
AND
GREAT

I am standing in a dimly lit room full of other humans, most of whom I have never met before. The space seems slightly too small for everyone to exist comfortably, just like the dress I'm wearing. The music is being played at a volume that all but eliminates the possibility of following a conversation, but what's odd is that when I look around I see half the people are doing very good 'I am definitely hearing what you are saying, taking it on board, and demonstrating my interest via the medium of nods' expressions. The other half are already pissed enough to believe them, and will continue talking about their Kickstarter campaign for a lo-fi film they are making about the time they spent backpacking in Thailand. We are all having a wonderful time and whose fucking idea was this anyway?

Sometimes I wish everyone would show up to stuff looking like they did 2 hours ago when they were at home, wearing a pyjama top and some old trackies they'd been absent-mindedly picking half a dried up old cornflake off of for half an hour as they finished binge watching another series of House of Game of Mad Cards. I just feel it would save a lot of time. When two people meet each other, instead of having to go through the whole SO WHAT DO YOU DO? faff where both parties fabricate information that'll make them appear Not Weird they could just point at each other's corn-flakes and go 'hah, yeah'.

But people are always asking, directly or otherwise, who you are and what do you do and what are you into and what are your opinions on this thing you would be stupid to have no opinions on. It's stuff that you're expected to have answers for, certainly as an adult. Whenever I meet someone with a strong personality I baulk, because working out what I am is hard. A combination of shit self-esteem and adolescence entirely subsumed by illness left me spat out feeling like an unfathomable question mark of a person in a world full of self-assured humans who appeared to know exactly what they were doing. It's been painstaking trying to slowly scrape enough bits of me back together and build new ones that I can use to anchor and contextualise myself and present to the outside world as being Mine. I've got a few, and relatively speaking I feel more of a Person than I used to, but that doesn't stop the emptiness from lingering like the clingy unwanted bastard that it is; poking holes in my certainty from time to time with its jabby little fingers and making me feel like a rather sad nubbin of Swiss cheese.

All I know is that I can't compare myself to others so acutely or live in terms of everything I'm not, because those are both pretty toxic ways to exist. As scary as it feels, I can only go from where I am today, right now, holding onto what I have so far and remembering that, just like everyone else, I am on my own trajectory, which is okay! And besides, I don't think anyone knows what the fuck's going on all of the time; some people are just better at pretending.

ARTICULATE DOG.

I'VE GOT A LOT
ON MY PLATE

(HIGHLY IRONIC) PIE CHART ABOUT EATING DISORDERS

NORMAL SERVING SIZE

WHAT I'LL ALLOW MYSELF TO EAT IN FRONT OF YOU

WHAT I'LL EAT LATER ON, ALONE, STRAIGHT OUT THE FRIDGE TO THE BACKDROP OF MY OWN ANXIETY AND LOATHING

OH AND THIS TOO, OF COURSE. I DON'T EVEN LIKE PIE. STUPID HELL CIRCLE.

FOOD THAT
IS LYING
ABOUT BEING
REAL·FOOD

~~RYVITA~~
RECTANGULAR TILES
OF COMPRESSED DUST

~~DIET CEREAL~~
OVERPRICED FLAKES
MADE IN HELL, OF HELL

SPESHAL
K
BUY THIS YOU
ARE FAT

~~LOW-FAT YOGHURT~~
OLD MILK STRIPPED OF
ALL JOY THAT IS THEN
AGGRESSIVELY MARKETED
AT WOMEN

MILK
NO

~~LOW-CALORIE READY MEALS~~
ABSOLUTELY NOT A MEAL.
MAINLY AN OLD PEA BOBBING
ABOUT IN UNIDENTIFIABLE
SAUCE. SMELLS OF DEATH
A BIT.

HEALTHY
VEGTBLEH
CURRY

~~ANYTHING THAT
DESCRIBES ITSELF AS
"LIGHT"~~
GET IT OUT OF MY HOUSE
HOME THIS INSTANT

NOTHING
O'S
LIGHT

LIES
LIGHT
SPREAD

HUNGER

OH, I SEE I AM
EXPERIENCING THE
PHYSICAL SENSATION
OF BEING HUNGRY.

PRE-PERIOD HUNGER

EVERYONE GET OUT OF
MY WAY I AM **DYING**.
MY STOMACH IS A
BOTTOMLESS
PIT AND I HAVE
TO EAT THE
ENTIRE SUN
RIGHT THIS
VERY INSTANT
OR I WILL SURELY
PERISH

IDEAL WITCH POWERS

FLAWLESS ESTIMATION
OF PASTA
QUANTITIES

THAT'S IT, THAT'S
ALL I WANT - TO NOT
END UP STARING AT
A SAD CLUMP OF
LEFTOVER YELLOW IN
THE PAN AND
CURSING MY INABILITY
TO DO ANYTHING
RIGHT EVERY TIME
I MAKE SPAGHETTI

*TERMS AND CONDITIONS APPLY. ABOVE
STATEMENT MAY NOT DEFINITELY WON'T
BE A FULL AND ACCURATE REFLECTION OF
HOW COMPLICATED MY RELATIONSHIP
WITH FOOD IS, AND HOW YEARS OF
EATING DISORDERS AND FOOD FUCKERY
HAVE LEFT ME WITH A BACKLOG OF
RESIDUAL ANXIETY OVER WHAT I DO
AND DON'T PUT ON MY PLATE

BUT HEY, YOU TRY AND FIT THAT ALL
IN ONE SENTENCE...

GOLDILOCKS & THE THREE BEARS (AND BULIMIA)

ONCE UPON AN UGH, A GIRL CALLED GOLDILOCKS STUMBLED ACROSS A HOUSE IN THE WOODS. SHE WANDERED INTO THE KITCHEN, AND THERE ON THE TABLE WERE THREE BOWLS OF PORRIDGE

SHE STARED AT THE PORRIDGE FOR A LONG TIME, WILLING HERSELF NOT TO EAT IT. BUT THE MORE SHE TOLD HERSELF "NO" THE MORE SHE WANTED TO EAT

IN THE END SHE SAT DOWN AND ATE THE FIRST BOWL.

AND THEN THE SECOND, NOT BOTHERING WITH THE SPOON THIS TIME

BY THE TIME THE
THIRD BOWL WAS
FINISHED, GOLDILOCKS
WAS FEELING VERY
FULL, OF FOOD AND
OF GUILT

THIS CAUSED SO MUCH PANIC SHE
FLUNG OPEN THE KITCHEN CUPBOARDS
AND SHOVELLED EVERYTHING THAT
WAS REMOTELY EDIBLE INTO HER MOUTH

WHEN THE OWNERS ARRIVED HOME AND DISCOVERED
THEIR BOMB-SITE OF A KITCHEN THEY LOOKED FOR THE
INTRUDER, AND FOUND GOLDILOCKS STUMBLING OUT THE
BATHROOM. THEY WERE SUITABLY PISSED OFF.

BEING BEARS, THEY HAD DECIDED TO EAT HER ON SIGHT,
BUT WHEN SHE SAT DOWN ON THE FLOOR AND BEGAN TO
CRY THEY PAUSED, UNABLE TO CONTEMPLATE SUCH
A SAD LOOKING MEAL

LUCKILY, THE SMALLEST BEAR HAD A PSYCHOLOGY DEGREE
AND HAPPENED TO BE A REGISTERED PSYCHOTHERAPIST
WITH HIS OWN SUCCESSFUL PRACTICE. HE TOOK GOLDILOCKS
GENTLY BY THE HAND AND POINTED TO THE BED BECAUSE
HE THOUGHT A LIE DOWN MIGHT DO HER GOOD.

"THERE", HE SAID

"YOU HAVE A LITTLE REST NOW AND BE KIND
TO YOURSELF, STRANGE FURLESS BEAR"

* POP! *

BRRT BRRT
BRRT
BRRT

HELLO, THIS IS A WAKE UP CALL.
YOU'RE DAMAGING YOUR BODY-
YOUR THROAT IS SCRATCHED TO BITS,
YOUR STOMACH ACHES, YOU'RE
SPENDING MOST OF YOUR MONEY
ON FOOD AND PILLS TO TRY AND
GET RID OF FOOD. THIS HAS TAKEN
OVER YOUR LIFE, IT NEEDS TO
STOP

FLING

How do I begin to describe what having an eating disorder is like? I could sit here and tell you horror stories about my experiences with anorexia, bulimia and binge eating. I could because I've been there done that and got the T-shirts in every single bloody size, but if you've ever had an eating disorder all that stuff will be very familiar anyway. And if you haven't, I don't want to cough up a load of misery porn at you written only in terms of dramatic weight loss or out of control calorie consumption. Those things are just some of the tangible manifestations of a very real and complex mental illness. I want to focus on the bit that happens above the shoulders; about what an eating disorder does to yer noggin.

So, putting aside the fact that I'm (shockingly) not a neuroscientist, let's call this the mind. (Yes, I know, I could have drawn a brain but I don't have time for that squiggly nonsense).

Typically, the mind will be occupied by a load of stuff – thoughts and opinions, hopes and fears, important relationships, things you're interested in and things you hate, experiences you've had and a bit of space for those you haven't, with all the usual mundane bollocks floating around in between.

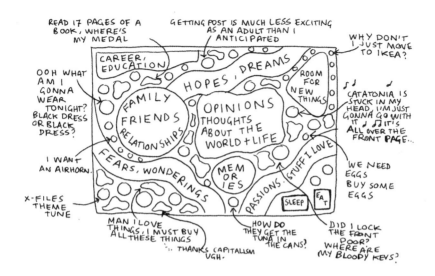

READ 17 PAGES OF A BOOK, WHERE'S MY MEDAL

GETTING POST IS MUCH LESS EXCITING AS AN ADULT THAN I ANTICIPATED

WHY DON'T I JUST MOVE TO IKEA?

OOH WHAT AM I GONNA WEAR TONIGHT? BLACK DRESS OR BLACK DRESS?

CAREER, EDUCATION

HOPES, DREAMS

FAMILY FRIENDS RELATIONSHIPS

OPINIONS THOUGHTS ABOUT THE WORLD + LIFE

ROOM FOR NEW THINGS

♪♪ CATATONIA IS STUCK IN MY HEAD, I'M JUST GONNA GO WITH IT ♪ ♫ IT'S ALL OVER THE FRONT PAGE...

I WANT AN AIRHORN.

FEARS, WONDERINGS

MEM OR IES

PASSIONS

STUFF I LOVE

WE NEED EGGS BUY SOME EGGS

X-FILES THEME TUNE

SLEEP

EAT

MAN I LOVE THINGS, I MUST BUY ALL THESE THINGS ... THANKS CAPITALISM UGH.

HOW DO THEY GET THE TUNA IN THE CANS?

DID I LOCK THE FRONT DOOR? WHERE ARE MY BLOODY KEYS?

In the bottom right hand corner I've shown a couple of the biological functions we are all pre-programmed to perform in order to stay alive. They don't take up a lot of thought-space because they should be pretty straight-forward. We get tired, we need rest, we sleep. We get hungry, the brain shouts 'oi muggins, make a sandwich or something', we eat the sandwich and we move on.

Something I think people don't often get is that eating disorders aren't really about losing weight or wanting to be thin. Yes, they are often de-fined by obsessive preoccupation with weight and food and very extreme, often dangerous behaviours around eating, but these are simply the phys-ical mediums through which deep underlying psychological distress is ex-pressed. This is why it's inaccurate to call anorexia 'a diet that spiralled out of control' or think of binge eating disorder and bulimia as problems attributable to laziness and lack of willpower around food. These are mental illnesses.

I was 14 when I first developed an eating disorder. I won't go into what the exact causes of this were (that's a whole other very complicated kettle of calorie-counted fish) but anorexia took hold very suddenly and aggressively on both my body and mind. After a while I began to struggle with binge eating and bulimia too, and I continued to fluctuate between these for years; sometimes very physically ill, sometimes less so, but always in a pretty consistently disordered mental state.

Here's a picture of what my mind looked like in the throes of illness.

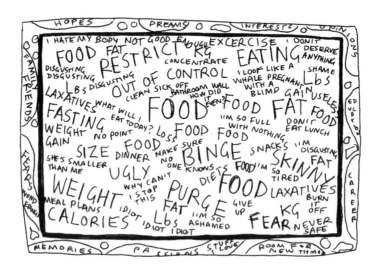

gets out pointy stick like they have in lectures So yep, as you can see the small 'want the sandwich make the sandwich eat the sandwich' area has grown wildly in size, pushing everything else of and about me to the very peripheries of my mind; its importance eclipsed entirely by eating and a barrage of associated eating related anxieties and self-loathing. There is very little space or energy left to invest in anything outside of that. And for me that's one of the most agonising realities of an eating disorder, being completely consumed by fear of what I am or am not consuming.

ANOREXIA, FOR AN ILLNESS SO CONCERNED WITH DEPRIVATION YOU ARE INCONCEIVABLY GREEDY

For months, while friends my age were worrying about their A levels or dealing with hangovers for the first time, I was sat behind a table at home or in hospital crying tears at a cheese sandwich like someone had asked me to eat a plate of rusty nails. And I couldn't count the number of occasions I cancelled seeing friends and turned work opportunities down because I had an important couple of meetings with the contents of the fridge and the toilet. It's like the most miserable, isolating full-time job ever.

Recovery is a word I handle with care, particularly when it comes to this stuff. For me it creates an unnecessary polarisation of 'illness' and 'wellness', when really the task of managing an eating disorder and reclaiming life back from it is a very non-linear and messy process with lots of intermediary and convalescence stages. I always had this fantasy that one day I'd wake up and things would go back to a happy healthy glowy normal. I'd skip about drinking green tea and eating handfuls of wholesome granola and be able to talk courageously of My Journey To Health.

Rather frustratingly, the physical, behavioural and mental progressions don't happen in synchronisation, so for lengthy periods of time I might have got myself physically 'well', but the behaviours and amount of space eating disordered thoughts took up in my mind were still extensive and profoundly distressing. Other times I'd develop really healthy and important insights into what was going on for me, but still be unable to utilise those in the face of entrenched and compulsive behaviours. And when I DID start making real headway, I was left with this huge nothingness in my mind where the eating disorder used to be, a daunting cavity I didn't know how the hell I would fill when the other stuff had been squashed out of existence for so long.

Basically what I'm saying is that this shit is complicated and takes ages.

It's been a series of attempts, battles and tiny, subtle victories (even if I haven't been jumping for joy at the time) – the first day I stopped forcing myself to drink scalding hot black coffees and thought 'fuck it, I'll put some normal non-ridiculous non-low fat milk in'; the first time I ate a regular meal in front of someone again instead of an 'oh that's alright I'm not very hungry' salad, and made it into bed that night without throwing any of it up; the first time I opened the kitchen cupboard fully intent on demolishing everything inside it, but managed to close the doors and go for a walk instead to come home feeling calmer. These may sound like inconsequential things, but for someone with an eating disorder they are akin to turning around and kicking the giant monster that's been chasing you for years on end squarely in the nads. These weren't epiphanies or concrete I AM NOW A RECOVERY moments, because the next time I was in these situations I wouldn't manage, and the time after I might only manage some of it. They weren't end points; they were subtle yet significant breakthroughs. And slowly (ever so slowly) as more and more of them trickled in, more and more life stuff could trickle in too and tip the balance back towards something more regular, both physically and emotionally.

It's been eight years since I was first diagnosed and my mind is pretty far into the process of refilling itself. I have residual issues and times where I struggle, but there is so much more going on in my mind outside of all that, and the world is opening up and happening at me from all sorts of new and interesting directions in a way that my eating disorder would have never allowed me to experience. Basically I am able to prioritise my life over strange feelings towards a sandwich, and for today that feels really good. That feels like enough.

WEIGHT LOSS TIPS FOR JANUARY

GET RID OF ALL
THE WEIGHT LOSS
ADVICE, THAT SHIT
WEIGHS A TON

TRY THESE NEW
GUILT-FREE
FOODS! . . .

BAD SCALES

GOOD SCALES

I DROP A VERY BIG BRICK ON THESE ONES

KERSMASH

BOOIOIOING

AH, FACE,

WE MEET AGAIN

TOO SHORT

TOO LONG

TOO TIGHT

TOO SHAPELESS

TOO JAZZY   NOT JAZZY ENOUGH

PERFECT CLOTHE

I AM SO LOVELY
LOVELY LOVLY

Those little things a girl can't leave ♡
♡ the house without !!

makeup!

a cute bag!

a spritz of her
favourite perfume

tiny party crab

laser eyes

PEW
PEW

ZZZAP

flame thrower

PAINTIN MY NAILS
DUM DE DUM

PAINTIN EM UP REAL
NICE YESSY YES YES

AH! LOOKIE THAT!
NOW TO DRY

. . .

I NEED TO LEAVE THE HOUSE IN TEN MINUTES
AGO AND MY PHONE IS RINGING AND I NEED
TWELVE WEES AND MY WHOLE EVERYWHERE
IS SUDDENLY ITCHY AND THERE IS A HAIR
IN MY EYEBALL · HELLO
SMUDGEVILLE

BRRT
BRRT

REGGULAR

ELEGGANT

MY FAVOURITE IS WHEN IT GETS
COLD ENOUGH TO WEAR MY
BIG COAT. THE POCKETS ARE
ROOMY ENOUGH FOR PENS AND
CRISPS AND A LARGE ROCK
PROBABLY, IF I WANTED. NO ONE
KNOWS WHAT I LOOK LIKE
UNDER HERE, I AM THE GIANT
INTIMIDATING SACK OF DARKNESS
I'VE ALWAYS DREAMED OF BEING

BOOTS

GO AWAYS

PISS OFFS

FUCK THE
SHUT UPS

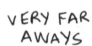

VERY FAR
AWAYS

INFINITIES

OTHER PEOPLE'S IDEAS OF MAKING AN EFFORT WITH SKIN CARE

DRINKING 28 LITRES OF WATER A DAY (MUST BE PURE, UNFILTERED, TRICKLED DOWN THE SIDE OF A MOUNTAIN AND ALSO BE GLUTEN FREE)

USING A VARIETY OF CLEANSERS, TONERS, BUFFERS, EXFOLIATERS AND FACE MASKS WHICH ARE ALL ANTI-AGEING ANTI-OXIDANT ANTI-MONEY SAVING AND MADE OF UNICORN JIZZ

MY IDEA OF MAKING AN EFFORT WITH SKIN CARE

SINGLE FACE PRODUCT WOT I DON'T REALLY KNOW WHAT IT IS BUT OK

SPLIDGE

SMEP

AH! I'M AN ANGEL!

BRA SHOPPING

AKA: THE ULTIMATE SOUL-CRUSHING ACTIVITY

BOOBS JUST WANNA ROAM FREE

BUT FOR PRACTICAL REASONS
(IE I DON'T WANT THEM TO FLY UP
AND SMACK ME IN THE FACE
ANY TIME I MOVE FASTER
THAN A CRAWL) I HAVE TO
CRAM MINE INTO AN OVER
THE SHOULDER BREAST PRISON

BREAST RECEPTACLES ARE SOLD IN A VARIETY
OF CRYPTIC SIZES ACCORDING TO AN ANCIENT
AND VIRTUALLY INDECIPHERABLE CODE OF
LETTERS AND NUMBERS. IT'S TIME TO START
RIFLING THROUGH HANGERS AND SWEARING
UNDER MY BREATH

CLUTCHING A MOUND OF BRA, I WADDLE TOWARDS
THE CHANGING ROOMS. FINDING THEM IS EASY;
I JUST MOVE IN THE DIRECTION OF THE SMELL
OF SWEAT AND ANGER AND THEN FOLLOW THE SIGHS

ONCE I'VE FOUGHT MY WAY INTO
MY OWN CURTAINED HELL-BOX
THAT'S WHEN THE FUN STARTS..

AND THIS IS ALL BEFORE I'VE
EVEN TRIED THE BLOODY BRAS ON

THERE ARE APPROXIMATELY
8693 THINGS THAT CAN GO WRONG
WITH A BRA. HERE IS A SMALL
SELECTION

#602 - WEIRD WONKY
CLEAVAGE AND THE
DREADED QUADRI - BOOB

#37 - DIGGY IN
SHOULDER STRAPS

#4462 - LOOKS GOOD,
IS THE PRICE OF A
SMALL YACHT

#3 - BACK SIZE
ALL WRONG

#80 - TOO MUCH
OF THIS

#10 - CUP SIZE
TOO ROOMY.
COULD A
COUPLE OF
EXTRA LEMONS
OR A TWIX IN
THERE

#81 - AND NOW
NOT ENOUGH OF THAT.

#551 MULTIWAYS
CONFUSED ABOUT
THEIR IDENTITY

MY BOOBS LOOK LIKE
THEY COULD PLAY A
MATRON IN A FILM
FROM THE 1930S

AFTER 20 MINUTES OF HEAVING MYSELF
IN AND OUT THE BASTARDS I MUST SIT
DOWN ON THE FLOOR IN A DESPAIR
BALL AND HAVE HAVE A LITTLE CRY

SOUL CRUSHING IS COMPLETE!

I'm stuck in a loveless affair with hating the way I look. My body should just be the place I live and walk around in and occasionally give things to like water and jam and antidepressants, but instead it's been transformed over the years into this huge, pervasive source of insecurity and fear. Don't get me wrong – I love spending hours at a time in front of the mirror making a comprehensive and damning mental list of everything that is wrong with my appearance, and having to try on no fewer than 8 different outfits before I find the one that makes me look the least like a potato; it's a delightful use of my time.

But even without chronically dysmorphic views and the knock-on effect an eating disorder has had on my self-image, it's pretty bloody hard to work out HOW we are meant to feel about ourselves. Of course no gender is exempt from the torrent of unhealthy and damaging ideals hurled at us left right and centre by the diet and beauty industries, they're very inclusive in their nastiness like that, but my experience of all this as a woman goes something like this: on the one hand we are insidiously and persistently shamed for being too fat and the wrong shape; two things which have been (wrongly) equated by society with laziness and unworthiness. Sadly I think I knew what a bingo wing was before I knew what the term misogyny meant so that says it all really. And then on the other hand we have these slightly newer ideals of loving yourself and feeling comfortable with how you look, and that the only right way to exist is by having a spectacularly harmonious and healthy relationship with one's body. We are simultaneously told to diet and indulge. We can't be fat but we can be 'curvy' or 'voluptuous' (shudder) IF, that is, we still fall within the bounds of what is deemed 'beautiful'. You can feel good about the way you look, but not before posting an Instagram photo of yourself sprinkling healthful protein dust onto a snot green smoothie with the caption, 'Just about to go for a 17 mile yoga jog!'. Navigating how to feel about my body feels akin to walking on a very narrow tightrope in high wind with 50ft drops on either side. It's impossible to get right.

People derive their sense of self-worth from all sorts of places – that thing you did and that experience you had and that friend who tells you you're not terrible. What happened to me from quite a young age, and certainly as I got older is that my brain decided to use my body as the focal point from which all my value as a person had to be measured. Everything became very black and white, very polarised. When I perceived myself as looking 'okay' (I could show you the imaginary 100 page document stipulating exactly what I meant by 'okay' but it wouldn't be very interesting) then I was a good person. I could permit myself a shred of confidence, at least enough to get dressed and go outside to exist around other humans. I had control. However, when I looked at myself and saw something 'incorrect' and not okay about my appearance, then I was a bad person. And bad person is a very understated way of saying 'A TERRIBLE BASTARD TRAINWRECK OF A PERSON. NOT EVEN 'A' TERRIBLE. THE **MOST** TERRIBLE. EVER. OF ALL TIME'. I wouldn't be able to get up. Plans would be cancelled. I'd feel out of control. It wasn't just that I felt bad, I became the bad.

Having every single decision I made or action I took dependent on how I perceived myself on that particular day (which, by the way, was entirely unpredictable) was exhausting, and pretty miserable. Extricating my sense of self-worth from my physical appearance is a long term project. Here are some things I've concluded about it though.

People don't give a toss what I look like, they've got their own stuff going on – No one is as hyper-aware and critical of my body as I am. That person on the bus is probably thinking about whether it'd look too keen to text them back yet, or how they are going get a bollocking when they show up to the meeting they're late for covered in toast crumbs. They might have had 'Orinoco Flow' by Enya stuck in their head since they woke up, or they might even be preoccupied with their own corporeal insecurities. I wouldn't know. But I do know that unless I rip all my clothes off and start running up and down the bus, people probably aren't going to register me for more than a few seconds. And they certainly won't be grossed out by the size of my thighs or shape of my face. That wouldn't make sense. I try to remember this when I'm getting the ol' paranoia brain.

I will see a lot more if I look a lot less – Being obsessed over my body and dedicating inordinate amounts of time and mental energy trying to make sure I look 'okay', sometimes through very unhealthy means, made my world very small. And very sad. There came a point where I became so fed up of chasing an ideal I could never really attain that I had to force myself away from the mirror, and away from all the body checking and Go And Look At Something Else, something other than me, just for a bit. Of course this way of thinking is not a switch I can suddenly flick. I'll still cancel plans from time to time when I can't stand my face, and sit on the floor of changing rooms crying because jeans are the devil's business, but what's different is that I get on with the rest now. The more stuff I'm able to do independent of the insecurities, the more confident I become that my experience of life does not have to be contingent on my body, it's a positive feedback loop of sorts.

So body, here's the thing: I don't really love you, but I'm going to let you be.

WHEN YOUR BODY CHANGES
(BECAUSE BODIES CHANGE)

DON'T KEEP OLD CLOTHES THAT DON'T FIT

TO USE AS OBJECTS TO MAKE YOURSELF FEEL BAD

YOU REALLY DON'T NEED TO STAND IN FRONT OF A MIRROR NAKED

YOU ARE FLUID, YOU ARE BENDY, YOU ARE YOURS!

MATCHY MATCHY

MATCHY
MATCHY

MATCHY MATCHY

I LIKE HAVING HAIRY LEGS

I CAN DO THIS

AND THIS

AND NOT BECAUSE I FEEL IT'S NECESSARY TO GO SHEARING,
YANKING AND DISSOLVING MY HAIR AWAY, IT'S NOT,
BUT SOMETIMES I DO LIKE HAVING THE LEGS OF SMOOTHNESS,
YOU KNOW SO I CAN BE ALL STREAMLINED

LIKE THIS

AND CAN ALSO USE MY CALF AS A RAMP FOR HOT WHEELS

HERE I AM DOING THE THING WITH MY JUMPER,
YOU KNOW, THE THING YOUR MOTHER TOLD YOU
NOT TO DO WHEN YOU WERE A CHILDREN.
BUT NOW I AM A GROWN UP AND SOLELY
RESPONSIBLE FOR THE JUMPERS I CAN DO IT
ALL I LIKE.

MMM,
STRETCHY
STRETCHY

I'M AN ADULT

I'M A GROAN UP

Everyone procrastinates, it's impossible not to. These days there's the endless snappagram twitblr facespleh scrollathons that must take place every 11 minutes or less (I sound old, I'm not old, I'm totally down with the kids). But it's got to be something that's always happened. All those fossils they've discovered of whateversauruses in rocks, it's not a coincidence that they're lying there with mouths wide open and limbs splayed out all panicky. I'm certain it's cos just before the meteorite hit they'd opened an envelope with their little dinosaur paws and seen it was a telephone bill so now they were lying face down on the Jurassic ground screeching 'I CAAAAAAN'T DOOOOO IIIIIIT…fuck it I'll just keep organising my rocks and scrolling through leaves'.

With me, avoidance of the task is more often than not associated with anxiety. Not always – sometimes I am just a bit tired or fed up (which, by the way, is allowed). But there's procrastination and then there's a fear of fucking up so monumental that it prevents me from getting anything done in the first place. And I'm not talking about particularly challenging things – basic forms, work-related emails, simple phone calls. My brain knows that objectively these tasks aren't huge, and won't even take that long, but whenever I'm presented with them my brain also decides it would be a fun idea to convert them into these great big monster worries, 18ft wide and twice as tall with jabby elbows and teeth as big as really big teeth. And so I do the only logical thing, which is lying face down on my bedroom ground screeching 'I CAAAAAAN'T DOOOOO IIIIIIT…fuck it better fire up the scrollin' thumbs it's time to enter the void'.

It's not even yer bog-standard single-layer anxiety, oh no, the effect of not being able to do anything results in another layer of fear centred around the thought, 'brilliant, first I can't do the thing, now everyone KNOWS I haven't done the thing and will think me a lazy useless bastard', which consequently leads to layer the third, perhaps the thickest and sludgiest of layers, which says 'Well maybe I AM a lazy useless bastard. EVERYONE ELSE is breezing through life and here I am, unable to do this tiny thing. Time to go and live in a cave'. This layer of reproachfulness and self-loathing is really what cements the underlying anxiety in place and makes it almost impossible for me to complete the original task.

I forget that I'm a capable human who just happens to have a very thinky brain, and see myself instead as this awful, ineffectual lump of idiot. It's a very horrible and isolating place to find myself. And like all these things, it's an uphill battle developing insight into what's going on and then trusting that insight enough to harness it positively.

Good news is that I'm making the porgress. I can do it now, I can on occasion tell the very harsh and punitive voice that really it needs to fuck off so I can work through the anxiety (or try to) but it's taken a long time to believe and reinforce the idea that my procrastination and avoidance is not often borne out of laziness or being a useless bastard, it's the result of overwhelming fear and very low self-esteem. And those things can't be ignored or denied, they exist and need to be given space before you can learn to override them. And once those layers start being separated and rationalised, it becomes a lot easier for me to maybe put my phone down, close the 5 wikipedia tabs about the history of zinc I have open on my laptop and just Get The Stuff Done.

ARTISTS WARM-UP

WAKE UP

STRETCH THOSE ART-MAKIN' HANDS

PRAY BRIEFLY TO THE GOD OF INSPIRATION

(HAHA THERE IS NO GOD)

BATHE IN AT LEAST 6 LITRES OF CAFFEINE

SIT DOWN AT YOUR VERY ORGANISED
AND CLEAN, INSTAGRAM WORTHY DESK
SO YOU CAN BEGIN

ONLY 6cm² OF
FREE WORKSPACE

BUT FIRST! CHECK ALL SOCIAL MEDIA SO
YOU CAN BE ~~JEALOUS~~ INSPIRED BY
ALL THE BRILLIANT WORK YOUR
PEERS
ARE
DOING. (THIS
TAKES 40 MINS
AT LEAST)

IT'S TIME TO DRAW! DON'T FORGET TO QUESTION
WHY YOU'RE DOING THIS AND WHETHER YOUR
ART HAS ANY VALUE OR WORTH.
IT'S FUN! YOU LOVE IT!

YOU'LL BE MAKING
GREAT WORK IN
NO TIME! *

* 8 HOURS

I JUST WANT TO BE A
BEAUTIFUL BUTTERFLY

BUT NO, APPARENTLY NOT. ADULTHOOD IS JUST
A LOAD OF RESPONSIBILITY AND WASHING
UP AND GO FUCK YOURSELF

WELL WHEN I'M AN
ADULT EVERYTHING WILL
BE FINE. I'LL BE CONFIDENT
AND KNOW WHAT I'M DOING
ABOUT ANYTHING AND NOT
BE SUCH   A POTATO

WHEN YOU'RE
AN ADULT?
YOU'RE 22

WELL SHIT A
BRICK SO I AM

EXCUSE ME WHILST
I GO AND SCREAM
AT THIS WALL

UMM THERE'S
NO WALL
OVER TH—

DOESN'T
MATTER

ARGHHHHHHHH

SO DO YOU
WORK OUT?

YESSSSS

SO FAR I'VE
WORKED OUT BREATHING,

HOW TO EAT AN
OFFENSIVE AMOUNT
OF CHEESE

AND THIS.

THINKING THINKING WITH
THE THING AND THE STUFF
AND OOH WHAT ABOUT TOAST..

DAMNIT, LOST MY
TRAIN OF THOUGHT

PFF, PROBABLY NOT
EVEN A TRAIN

PROBABLY ONE OF THOSE
REMOTE CONTROL HELICOPTERS
THAT LOOK FUN BUT ARE
ACTUALLY JUST HOVERING
DISASTER
RECEPTACLES
YOU CAN'T
CONTROL...

MY THOUGHT
PATTERNS

NYOOOOM

NYAAAHWWW

AHAHAH
HAHARGHHH
WHAT THE FUCK IS
GO ON?!?

WHOOSH

KERSMASH

NAPS ARE EITHER PERFECT..

COMFIEST, COSIEST, WARMEST LITTLE DOZEY BUN

I LOOK .. ADORABLE

WAKING UP FEELING CALM AND REFRESHED

I AM THE ANGEL OF SNOOZE

,, OR AN UNPRECEDENTED DIABOLICAL DISASTER

ALREADY EXHAUSTED AND ON THE BRINK OF COLLAPSE

UNDER THE ILLUSION SLEEP WILL CURE EVERYTHING

BODY ALL UNCOMFORTABLE AND TO FUCK

FALLING INTO A FROWNY SLUMBER

CRAZY HAIR

WAKING UP 3 HOURS LATER NOT KNOWING WHERE OR WHAT I AM AND I'M LATE FOR THE THING AND MY NECK IS SORE AND MY LEG WON'T WAKE UP

WHAT IS HAPPENING

TOO HOT AND COLD AND TIRED AND HUNGRY BUT SICK ALL AT ONCE

THERE IS NO INBETWEEN

SO YOUR BIRTHDAY'S COMING UP THEN! WHAT DO YOU WANT?

NOT MUCH.. JUST TO NOT BE REMINDED OF THE PASSING OF TIME IN A WAY THAT DENOTES HOW LITTLE I'VE ACHIEVED OVER THE LAST 12 MONTHS AND FOR IT TO BE LESS MISERABLE THAN THE LAST 6000 BIRTHDAYS, ALTHOUGH I WILL INEVITABLY SPEND THE DAY IN THE DARK, CRYING AND AVOIDING MYSELF VIA THE MEDIUM OF ALCOHOL

·· OH

SO VOUCHERS?!

SIGH YEH THAT'D BE LOVELY

INSTANT COFFEE

DELAYED COFFEE

"WHAT'LL YOU HAVE?"

LOW-KEY
"NO REALLY
I'M FINE"
SAD

SAD AS A SAD
THING BUT GONNA
BE SOPHISTICATED
ABOUT IT

FUCK HOLIDAYS
GIVE ME MORE
EVERYTHING THAT
IS BAD FOR ME SAD

HAHA I AM SAD BUT NOT
PAYING FOR ANY OF THIS
SHIT SO I'LL HAVE TWELVETY
OF WHATEVER THESE ARE.
WEHAY WATCH ME CATCH
MY TEARS IN THIS TINY
NOVELTY UMBRELLA!

I AM VERY SAD AND
WOULD PREFER NOT
TO FEEL MY OWN FACE
RIGHT NOW. THANKS

RIGHT!
THAT'S IT

I AM GOING TO
BED EARLY

BECAUSE IT'S BETTER
FOR ME..

..YES. I'LL WAKE UP EARLY
AND BE PRODUCTIVE AS FUCK
AND GO JOGGING WHILST I
EAT PORRIDGE
IN THE SHOWER
LIKE A
REAL
PERSON

EVERYOOONE LISTEN!
I AM GOING TO BED
EARLY!

IT'S 1:30 AM

COLLECTION OF THINGS I'VE SEEN WHILST MY EYES ARE GLUED TO THE FLOOR WITH SHYNESS ADHESIVE

GUM IN VARYING STAGES OF SQUISHY DECAY

DISCARDED RECEIPT MAKING OUT WITH A CIGARETTE BUTT

YOU INCOMPETENT BASTARD

PERSONAL REVELATION

TINY FLOOR BUNNY (EXCEPT NOT REALLY, THAT'S JUST WISHFUL THINKING AND LIES)

SOMETIMES I'LL BE OUT

..STROLLIN, STROLLIN..

LOVERLY DAY

..AND THEN SUDDENLY!

WAIT.. DID I LOCK THE FRONT DOOR??

DID I TAKE MY MEDICATION?

DID I SET THE TOASTER ON FIRE

DID I TURN THE TAP OFF??

IS MY HEAD STILL ATTACHED TO MY BODY? DID I LEAVE MY ARM ON THE BUS??

BEFORE I KNOW IT I'M SCRABBLING AROUND FRANTICALLY, CHECKING POCKETS..

SHIT WHERE'S MY PHONE??!

OH

I'M A WALKING BAG O'PANIC

RULES

PLEASE
KEEP YOUR FEET
OFF THE GRASS

PLEASE DO NOT
SCREAM AT THE GRASS
FOR BEING A BETTER
PERSON THAN YOU

IF YOU ARE A COUPLE
NEWLY IN LOVE **PLEASE**
TAKE YOUR OBNOXIOUS
COUPLINESS ELSEWHERE
YOU ARE _RUINING_ IT FOR
THE LONELY PEOPLE

PLEASE SHOW YOUR
RESPECT FOR NATURE
BY ROLLING AROUND
IN THE LEAVES SHOUTING
'PARKLIFE' AT REGULAR
INTERVALS

NO-ONE WANTS TO
HEAR ABOUT HOW THAT
CLOUD LOOKS LIKE A
HEDGE TRIMMER, _MOIRA_

PLEASE
GIVE SUNNY PATCH
PRIORITY TO DOGS.
THEY DESERVE IT

IN THE ANTARCTIC, PENGUINS HUDDLE
TOGETHER IN TIGHTLY PACKED GROUPS
TO CONSERVE HEAT AND SHELTER
THEMSELVES FROM INTENSE WINDS

IN THE LONDON, PEOPLE HUDDLE
UNDER THE LEAKY BUS SHELTER MUCH
LIKE PENGUINS EXCEPT WE ARE
ALL ANGRY AND HATE EACH OTHER

WAYS TO FEEL IN CONTROL WHEN YOUR LIFE IS DOING BIG CHANGES

YOU WILL HAVE MANY ESSENTIAL, COMPLICATED THINGS TO SORT OUT. IT IS IMPORTANT YOU DO THEM. NOW.

17 MISSED CALLS
∞ EMAILS

mmmmm fuvvuck

UNCERTAIN FUCKERY

ADULT SHIT I DON'T UNDERSTAND

DOCUMENTS

... SO INSTEAD!

NEGLECT RESPONSIBILITY AND FOCUS ON ARRANGING TINY ORNAMENTS ON A SHELF FOR HALF AN HOUR AND SIMILARLY UNPRODUCTIVE POINTLESS TASKS. THAT WAY NOTHING GETS DONE AND YOU HAVE CONTROL OVER MICRO-AREAS OF YOUR LIFE

THEN DRINK SO MUCH CAFFEINE YOU CAN'T FEEL YOUR OWN EYES. IT'S GOING TO BE FINE

RELAX   OKAY   THAT'S TOO MUCH
                                                        RELAX

WE'RE
ALL
ABSOLUTELY
FINE

IT'S LOVELY SEEING PEOPLE BUT I CANNOT
WAIT FOR THEM TO LEAVE SO I CAN BE
MYSELF AGAIN AND EAT CRACKERS ALONE
IN THE DARK

THIS IS HOW IT FEELS WHEN SOMEONE CLAIMS TO KNOW
EXACTLY WHAT YOU'RE GOING THROUGH INSTEAD OF JUST
LISTENING TO WHAT YOU'RE SAYING

DATE

I'M EATING FOOD I DON'T LIKE
WITH A MAN I DON'T GET
IN A DRESS THAT'S TOO SMALL
I LIKE MY SHOES
BUT I COULD HAVE LIKED MY SHOES AT HOME
ALONE
IN FRONT OF THE TV

WITH CRISPS

WHAT ARE YOU LOOKING AT SON?

THAT'S ONLY
SOME AIR

MY GIRLFRIEND

 I KNOW

BRRT BRRT

HELLOO?

SHIT SHIT SHIT ·.

OH HEEY, HOW ARE YOU?

MY HEAD IS AN ACTUAL TOILET ·.

AH, NOT TOO BAD THANKS, GOING ALONG

SHITTING SHITTING SHIT ·.

YES IT'S BEEN TOO LONG! LET ME JUST CHECK WHEN I'M FREE

..OOH I'M PRETTY BUSY, WEEKEND MIGHT WORK?

MON - PANIC ATTACK	THURS - PANIC ATTACK : THE SEQUEL
TUES - BODY HORROR DAY	FRI - EXISTENTIAL CRISIS
WEDS ~ CRYING FESTIVAL	SAT/SUN - MEH DUNNO

I'M A FOOL, A DAMNDED FOOL ·.

GREAT! SATURDAY IT IS. SEE YA THEN!

SATURDAY

I'M A TINY .VERY LARGE DISASTER

HOW TO GET FRIENDS

FIND PEOPLE WITH SIMILAR INTERESTS

SHARE RELATABLE INTERNET CONTENT

WIN THEIR AFFECTIONS WITH CRISPS

OR FAILING THAT
JUST BECOME A FREE WIFI HOTSPOT

HOW TO TAKE A
COMPLIMENT

) TAKE THE THING WHILST
BLUSHING PROFUSELY

HERE! A NICE
ABOUT
YOU!

A
NICE

② CLUTCH IT GINGERLY. THIS IS
AN ALIEN CONCEPT THAT DOES
NOT CORRELATE WITH
PERSONAL CONVICTIONS THAT
I AM A COMPLETE
TROWEL

A
NICE

) RESIST TEMPTATION TO SCREAM
"NO NO NOoo THIS IS A GIANT
ERROR YOU HAVE MADE"

A
NICE

④

HAPPY THANKLEMAS
TO YOU TOO.
YES.
HELLO

NICE

GOD I FEEL SO WORRIED
WHEN I START LIKING
SOMEONE

THE 'AM I ALLOWED TO
ENJOY MYSELF AND FEEL
VALUED AS A PERSON'

THE SUDDEN UNEXPECTED
BOUTS OF ELATION MIXED
WITH TERROR OVER FEELINGS FOR
ANOTHER PERSON THEM
DICTATING
MY THOUGHTS
AND
BEHAVIOUR..

.. KYLIE WAS RIGHT,
I REALLY **CAN'T**
GET YOU OUT OF MY
HEAD

AND THE REJECTION,
THE CONSTANT, LOOMING
POTENTIAL FOR REJECTION

BECAUSE AFTER ALL IT'S
ONLY A MATTER OF TIME
BEFORE THEY GET SICK OF MY
FAT UGLY WHINE HOLE OF A
FACE

I SUPPOSE THE ANSWER
REALLY IS TO STAY WELL
AWAY FROM
OTHER
PEOPLE

TO NEVER ALLOW MYSELF
TO BECOME VULNERABLE

YES, NOW I AM FREE
OF ANY INTERPERSONAL
STRESS.
HOORAY!

I AM SO, SO,
VERY ALONE

I'M NOT CLINGY

IT'S JUST MY EAR,
SHE IS TIRED

CAN I GO?

..NO

IF YOUR PERSON LEFT
YOU..

JUST KNOW THAT
THERE ARE PLENTY
MORE FISH IN THE SEA..

..AND THEY'RE ALL IN LOVING, STABLE
RELATIONSHIPS

AND YOU ARE STILL DESPERATELY
ALONE. SO..SO LONELY.. SO VERY..

AH SHUDDUP
STUPID
COMIC
NARRATION

HEHE..

WE ARE FRIENDS

WE SHARE EVERYTHING

CRISPS

A LOVE OF
TASTELESS HATS

CRIPPLING
FEAR OF REALITY
AND EVERYTHING
IN IT

SO HOW ARE YA?

WHEN LIFE GIVES YOU LEMON

TYING UP LOOSE ENDS

OUTRODUCTION BIT

So yep, life's stupid sometimes. It's like someone handed you a nice yoghurt and then said you can only eat the nice yoghurt with a fork; incredibly fiddly, takes ages, you look like a twat trying to work it out AND it causes you to start making bad metaphors involving dairy products. Great.

I digress... this is the end of the thing you've been reading. And now you're going to go off and do something else. Maybe it's a good day and you're feeling on top of things and there's A Nice planned and existing feels relatively easy. Maybe it's a bad day, end of the world levels of bad even, a sad soggy salty pillow sort of time is occurring. Maybe you can't put your finger on what's going on but you know it's A LOT or maybe you're having no discernible type of day at all, floating about neither here nor meh. But we are doing it, in one way or another. Life's happening at us and we're all bobbling along to our various degrees like the crying, laughing, very sentient potato weirdos that we are. I'm not actually that great at endings (again, see above with the whole life yoghurt thing) but I'll leave this last drawing here, just in case you need it.

WHAT DID YOU
DO TODAY?

...

MANAGED

ACKNOWLEDGEMENTS BIT

I would like to thank everyone at Orion and Trapeze who was mad enough to say Yes and then help me bring this book to life and launch it (very skilfully) at the world with such dedication and enthusiasm, and in particular Emma Smith for editin' it and telling me when I have green pen on my face. A huge fuck-off sized thank you to Nicola Barr for being a relentlessly brilliant human and agent; and to Andy for making that phone call. Thanks also to Christopher Schelling and Patty Rice for all their hard work over in The States or 'The States' as we call it in UK English.

I am incredibly grateful to everyone that has watched and heard and responded to me burping my art out online over the years in the most wonderfully kind and consistently supportive way, more than I am able to articulate in words actually so, if that is you: know that you are just great and have this

There are many (too many to list) NHS professionals and hospitals that have supported me through some extremely difficult years and hovered around with me on the brink until I've been ready to step back. It's a very long haul, but I am getting there; thank you.

There are a few brilliant people who listened to me moan and worry about this book most days for well over a year and continued to encourage the shit out of me when I needed it most; I think it will sound cool and mysterious to say YOU KNOW WHO YOU ARE so that is what I am saying and I will be yelling and pointing to this paragraph when I see you next.

I would like to thank my dog, Sadie, for tolerating me.

And finally my family, who are the funniest people I've ever met and have just been Getting It for so many years. Me being able to write this book is, in many ways, all of your faults. So yeah, thanks for that.

This edition first published in Great Britain in 2016
by Trapeze
an imprint of the Orion Publishing Group Ltd
Carmelite House
50 Victoria Embankment
London EC4Y 0DZ
An Hachette UK Company

1 3 5 7 9 10 8 6 4 2

A CIP catalogue record for this book
is available from the British Library.

ISBN: 978 1 4091 6729 7

Printed in Italy